T0084332

Easy Concert Pieces
Leichte Konzertstücke

for Descant (Soprano) Recorder and Piano
für Sopranblockflöte und Klavier

Volume 1 / Band 1

30 Pieces from 5 Centuries
30 Stücke aus 5 Jahrhunderten

Grade / Schwierigkeitsgrad:
very easy to easy / sehr leicht bis leicht

Edited by / Herausgegeben von
Elisabeth Kretschmann

ED 23043
ISMN 979-0-001-20532-0

Volume 2 / Band 2:
easy to intermediate / leicht bis mittelschwer
ED 23044

Volume 3 / Band 3:
intermediate / mittelschwer
ED 23162

www.schott-music.com

Mainz · London · Madrid · Paris · New York · Tokyo · Beijing
© 2020 Schott Music GmbH & Co. KG, Mainz · Printed in Germany

Preface

This series of *Easy Concert Pieces* presents easy to intermediate pieces for descant recorder, including original compositions alongside arrangements in a selection ranging across different eras. These pieces will provide an ideal complement to any recorder tutorial method: as well as providing material for tuition purposes they are particularly suitable for playing at auditions, competitions and examinations. Pieces are grouped in increasing order of difficulty in three volumes. Within each book pieces are presented in chronological order, starting with works from the Renaissance and early Baroque period and progressing through Baroque, Classical and Romantic periods to more modern music.

Book 1 contains short and easily manageable pieces with a range from c' to e" including semitones f#' and b♭'. Rhythms are kept simple. Some of the pieces have a very limited range, so this book can be used as a source of material very soon after starting recorder lessons.

Book 2 extends the range of notes to a" and includes a few semitones. Pieces are rhythmically more complex and slightly more demanding with regard to fingering technique and melodic expression than the pieces in book 1.

Book 3 finally includes pieces using the whole range of notes. Longer pieces allow for more detailed musical phrasing with scope for individual interpretation and expression.

The accompanying CD includes all the pieces in the full version and as play-along piano accompaniment, too.

Elisabeth Kretschmann
Translation Julia Rushworth

Vorwort

Die Reihe *Easy Concert Pieces* enthält leichte bis mittelschwere Originalkompositionen sowie Bearbeitungen für Sopranblockflöte und Klavier und bietet einen Querschnitt durch verschiedene Epochen. Die ausgewählten Werke sind eine ideale Ergänzung zu jeder Blockflötenschule. Neben dem Unterricht eignen sie sich besonders gut für Vorspiele, Wettbewerbe und Prüfungen. Die Stücke wurden für die 3 Bände nach aufsteigendem Schwierigkeitsgrad angeordnet. Innerhalb eines Bandes finden sich die Werke in chronologischer Reihenfolge, angefangen bei Werken aus Renaissance und Frühbarock über Barock, Klassik und Romantik bis hin zu modernen Stücken.

In Band 1 befinden sich überschaubare kurze Stücke im Tonraum von c' bis e" einschließlich der Halbtöne fis' und b'. Die Rhythmik ist einfach gehalten. Einige Stücke haben nur einen geringen Ambitus, so dass dieser Band schon nach kurzer Zeit des Blockflötenunterrichts als Begleitheft Verwendung finden kann.

In Band 2 wird der Tonraum bis a" erweitert, einschließlich einiger Halbtöne. Die Werke sind rhythmisch komplexer gestaltet und stellen in Grifftechnik und melodischem Ausdruck etwas höhere Anforderungen als die Stücke aus Band 1.

In Band 3 wurden schließlich Werke aufgenommen, die den gesamten Tonraum nutzen. Die teils längeren Stücke ermöglichen eine musikalisch differenzierte Arbeit und fördern die eigene Interpretation und Ausdrucksstärke.

Die beigefügte CD enthält alle Stücke als Vollversion und als Klavierbegleitung zum Mitspielen.

Elisabeth Kretschmann

Impressum
Cover photography: © Mollenhauer-Blockflöten
CD: Elisabeth Kretschmann, Descant (Soprano) Recorder, Volker Krebs (Piano)
Recording: Studio Tonmeister, Mainz (Nos. 1, 3–4, 9, 15–16, 24–30) /
Gunni Mahling, Saarbrücken (Nos. 2, 5–8, 10–14, 17–23)
© 2020 Schott Music GmbH & Co. KG, Mainz
Printed in Germany · BSS 59385

Contents / Inhalt

pitch a / Stimmton a (Track No. 61)

1. Galliarde

Pierre Attaingnant
ca. 1494–1552
Arr.: Elisabeth Kretschmann

2. Rondo

Tilman Susato
1500–1562
Arr.: Elisabeth Kretschmann

3. Almande

Pierre Phalèse
ca. 1510 – ca. 1583
Arr.: Elisabeth Kretschmann

4. Burate Galliarde

Pierre Phalèse
Arr.: Vera Mohrs

5. Bourrée 1

Michael Praetorius
1571–1621
Arr.: Elisabeth Kretschmann

Bourrée 2

6. Bourrée 2

Michael Praetorius
Arr.: Elisabeth Kretschmann

D. C. Bourrée 1 ad lib.
(senza ripetizione)

7. La Bergamasca

Marco Uccellini
1603–1680
Arr.: Elisabeth Kretschmann

*) 4 bars piano prelude ad lib. / 4 Takte Klaviervorspiel ad lib.

8. Argeers

John Playford
1623–1686
Arr.: Vera Mohrs

9. Gathering Peascods

John Playford
Arr.: Max Volbers

from / aus: J. Playford, The English Dancing Master. 5 Easy Dances, Schott SE 1018

10. Minuet / Menuett

Johann Fischer
1646–1716
Arr.: Vera Mohrs

11. Air

Michel-Richard Delalande
1657–1726
Arr.: Vera Mohrs

12. Contredance

Michel-Richard Delalande
Arr.: Vera Mohrs

13. Allegro

from: Spring / aus: Der Frühling

Antonio Vivaldi
1678–1741
Arr.: Peter Mohrs

from / aus: A. Vivaldi, The Four Seasons / Die vier Jahreszeiten, op. 8/1

Easy Concert Pieces
Leichte Konzertstücke

for Descant (Soprano) Recorder and Piano
für Sopranblockflöte und Klavier

Volume 1 / Band 1

30 Pieces from 5 Centuries
30 Stücke aus 5 Jahrhunderten

Grade / Schwierigkeitsgrad:
very easy to easy / sehr leicht bis leicht

Edited by / Herausgegeben von
Elisabeth Kretschmann

ED 23043
ISMN 979-0-001-20532-0

Volume 2 / Band 2:
easy to intermediate / leicht bis mittelschwer
ED 23044

Volume 3 / Band 3:
intermediate / mittelschwer
ED 23162

Descant (Soprano) Recorder

www.schott-music.com

Mainz · London · Madrid · Paris · New York · Tokyo · Beijing
© 2020 Schott Music GmbH & Co. KG, Mainz · Printed in Germany

Preface

This series of *Easy Concert Pieces* presents easy to intermediate pieces for descant recorder, including original compositions alongside arrangements in a selection ranging across different eras. These pieces will provide an ideal complement to any recorder tutorial method: as well as providing material for tuition purposes they are particularly suitable for playing at auditions, competitions and examinations. Pieces are grouped in increasing order of difficulty in three volumes. Within each book pieces are presented in chronological order, starting with works from the Renaissance and early Baroque period and progressing through Baroque, Classical and Romantic periods to more modern music.

Book 1 contains short and easily manageable pieces with a range from c' to e" including semitones f#' and bb'. Rhythms are kept simple. Some of the pieces have a very limited range, so this book can be used as a source of material very soon after starting recorder lessons.

Book 2 extends the range of notes to a" and includes a few semitones. Pieces are rhythmically more complex and slightly more demanding with regard to fingering technique and melodic expression than the pieces in book 1.

Book 3 finally includes pieces using the whole range of notes. Longer pieces allow for more detailed musical phrasing with scope for individual interpretation and expression.

The accompanying CD includes all the pieces in the full version and as play-along piano accompaniment, too.

Elisabeth Kretschmann
Translation Julia Rushworth

Vorwort

Die Reihe *Easy Concert Pieces* enthält leichte bis mittelschwere Originalkompositionen sowie Bearbeitungen für Sopranblockflöte und Klavier und bietet einen Querschnitt durch verschiedene Epochen. Die ausgewählten Werke sind eine ideale Ergänzung zu jeder Blockflötenschule. Neben dem Unterricht eignen sie sich besonders gut für Vorspiele, Wettbewerbe und Prüfungen. Die Stücke wurden für die 3 Bände nach aufsteigendem Schwierigkeitsgrad angeordnet. Innerhalb eines Bandes finden sich die Werke in chronologischer Reihenfolge, angefangen bei Werken aus Renaissance und Frühbarock über Barock, Klassik und Romantik bis hin zu modernen Stücken.

In Band 1 befinden sich überschaubare kurze Stücke im Tonraum von c' bis e" einschließlich der Halbtöne fis' und b'. Die Rhythmik ist einfach gehalten. Einige Stücke haben nur einen geringen Ambitus, so dass dieser Band schon nach kurzer Zeit des Blockflötenunterrichts als Begleitheft Verwendung finden kann.

In Band 2 wird der Tonraum bis a" erweitert, einschließlich einiger Halbtöne. Die Werke sind rhythmisch komplexer gestaltet und stellen in Grifftechnik und melodischem Ausdruck etwas höhere Anforderungen als die Stücke aus Band 1.

In Band 3 wurden schließlich Werke aufgenommen, die den gesamten Tonraum nutzen. Die teils längeren Stücke ermöglichen eine musikalisch differenzierte Arbeit und fördern die eigene Interpretation und Ausdrucksstärke.

Die beigefügte CD enthält alle Stücke als Vollversion und als Klavierbegleitung zum Mitspielen.

Elisabeth Kretschmann

Contents / Inhalt

pitch a / Stimmton a (Track No. 61)

1. Galliarde

Pierre Attaingnant
ca. 1494–1552

2. Rondo

Tilman Susato
1500–1562

3. Almande

Pierre Phalèse
ca. 1510–ca. 1583

4. Burate Galliarde

Pierre Phalèse

5. Bourrée 1

Michael Praetorius
1571–1621

Bourrée 2

6. Bourrée 2

Michael Praetorius

D. C. Bourrée 1 ad lib.
(senza ripetizione)

7. La Bergamasca

Marco Uccellini
1603–1680

*) 4 bars piano prelude ad lib. / 4 Takte Klaviervorspiel ad lib.

8. Argeers

John Playford
1623–1686

9. Gathering Peascods

John Playford

from / aus: J. Playford, The English Dancing Master. 5 Easy Dances, Schott SE 1018

10. Minuet / Menuett

Johann Fischer
1646–1716

11. Air

Michel-Richard Delalande
1657–1726

12. Contredance

Michel-Richard Delalande

13. Allegro

from: Spring / aus: Der Frühling

Antonio Vivaldi
1678–1741

from / aus: A. Vivaldi, The Four Seasons / Die vier Jahreszeiten, op. 8/1

14. Bourrée

Georg Friedrich Händel
1685–1759

from / aus: G. F. Händel, The Water Music / Wassermusik

15. Minuet / Menuett 1

Jacques Aubert
1689–1753

Minuet 2

16. Minuet / Menuett 2

Jacques Aubert

D.C. Minuet 1 ad. lib.

17. Bourrée

Johann Adolf Hasse
1699–1783

18. Bourlesque

Leopold Mozart
1719–1787

19. A Little Night Music / Eine kleine Nachtmusik

(Theme / Thema)

Wolfgang Amadeus Mozart
1756–1791

Allegro (♩ ca. 112)

© 2020 Schott Music GmbH & Co. KG, Mainz

20. Ode to Joy
„Freude schöner Götterfunken"

Ludwig van Beethoven
1770–1827

♩ ca. 108

© 2020 Schott Music GmbH & Co. KG, Mainz

from / aus: L. van Beethoven, Symphony No. 9 / Symphonie Nr. 9

21. La donna è mobile

Giuseppe Verdi
1813–1901

from / aus: G. Verdi, Rigoletto   *) Original: always /immer: ♫

22. Cancan

Jacques Offenbach
1819–1880

from / aus: J. Offenbach, Orpheus in the Underworld / Orpheus in der Unterwelt

23. Guten Abend, gut' Nacht

Johannes Brahms
1840–1893

24. Moderato

Hans Poser
1917–1970

from / aus: H. Poser, 10 kleine Stücke (No. 6), Möseler MOS 41001

25. Allegro

Carl Orff
1895–1982
Arr.: Hermann Regner

from / aus: Orff-Schulwerk, Recorder Book / Flötenbuch, Schott ED 9248

26. Town in the Sunshine

Leslie Searle
*1937

from / aus: L. Searle, For my Friends. 12 Easy Pieces / 12 leichte Stücke, Schott SE 1052

27. Chilling at Noon
Chillen am Mittag

Rainer Mohrs
*1953

from / aus: B. Hintermeier, Blockflöte spielen – mein schönstes Hobby, Spielbuch 1, Schott ED 22381

28. Great Balloon Trip
Große Ballonfahrt

Rainer Mohrs

from / aus: B. Hintermeier, Blockflöte spielen – mein schönstes Hobby, Band 1, Schott ED 22151

29. Walking by the Sea
Spaziergang am Meer

Mike Schönmehl
*1957

from / aus: M. Schönmehl, Fun with Jazz Flute, Schott ED 8881

30. The Errant Knight
on the Wrong Track
Der fahrende Ritter auf Irrwegen

Almuth Werner
*1968

from / aus: A. Werner, Flaviermusik, First Sparkling Duets / Erste spritzige Duette, Zimmermann, ZM 35780

14. Bourrée

Georg Friedrich Händel
1685–1759
Arr.: Vera Mohrs

from / aus: G. F. Händel, The Water Music / Wassermusik

15. Minuet / Menuett 1

Jacques Aubert
1689–1753
Arr.: Anne Melzer

Minuet 2

16. Minuet / Menuett 2

Jacques Aubert
Arr.: Anne Melzer

D.C. Minuet 1 ad. lib.

17. Bourrée

Johann Adolf Hasse
1699–1783
Arr.: Alfred Moffat

18. Bourlesque

Leopold Mozart
1719–1787
Arr.: Vera Mohrs

19. A Little Night Music / Eine kleine Nachtmusik

(Theme / Thema)

Wolfgang Amadeus Mozart
1756–1791
Arr.: Elisabeth Kretschmann

Allegro (♩ ca. 112)

20. Ode to Joy / „Freude schöner Götterfunken"

Ludwig van Beethoven
1770–1827
Arr.: Wolfgang Birtel

from / aus: L. van Beethoven, Symphony No. 9 / Symphonie Nr. 9

21. La donna è mobile

Giuseppe Verdi
1813–1901
Arr.: Vera Mohrs

from / aus: G. Verdi, Rigoletto

*) Original: always / immer

22. Cancan

Jacques Offenbach
1819–1880
Arr.: Vera Mohrs

from / aus: J. Offenbach, Orpheus in the Underworld / Orpheus in der Unterwelt

23. Guten Abend, gut' Nacht

Johannes Brahms
1840–1893
Arr.: Vera Mohrs

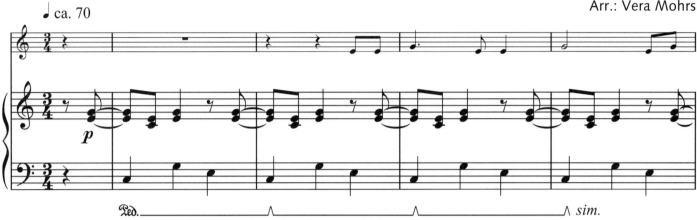

24. Moderato

Hans Poser
1917–1970

Swinging / Schwingend (♩. ca. 68)

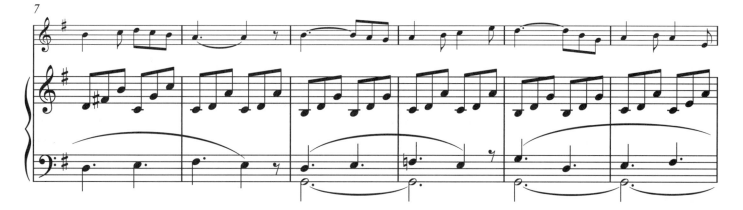

from / aus: H. Poser, 10 kleine Stücke (No. 6), Möseler MOS 41001

25. Allegro

Carl Orff
1895–1982
Arr.: Hermann Regner

from / aus: Orff-Schulwerk, Recorder Book / Flötenbuch, Schott ED 9248

26. Town in the Sunshine

Leslie Searle
*1937

Moderate Waltz (♩ = 152)

from / aus: L. Searle, For my Friends. 12 Easy Pieces / 12 leichte Stücke, Schott SE 1052

27. Chilling at Noon / Chillen am Mittag

Rainer Mohrs
*1953

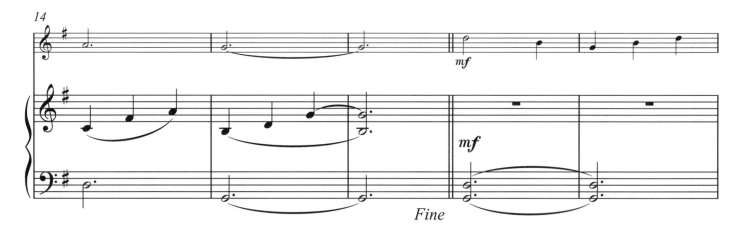

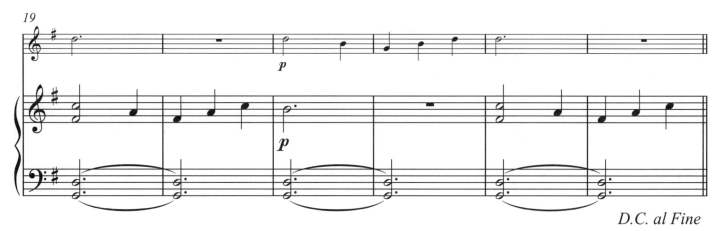

from / aus: B. Hintermeier, Blockflöte spielen – mein schönstes Hobby, Spielbuch 1, Schott ED 22381

28. Great Balloon Trip / Große Ballonfahrt

Rainer Mohrs

from / aus: B. Hintermeier, Blockflöte spielen – mein schönstes Hobby, Band 1, Schott ED 22151

29. Walking by the Sea / Spaziergang am Meer

Mike Schönmehl
*1957

from / aus: M. Schönmehl, Fun with Jazz Flute, Schott ED 8881

30. The Errant Knight on the Wrong Track /
Der fahrende Ritter auf Irrwegen

Almuth Werner
*1968

from / aus: A. Werner, Flaviermusik, First Sparkling Duets / Erste spritzige Duette, Zimmermann, ZM 35780

*) *Glissando* across the keys with one hand. The hand can be protected thereby with a piece of cloth or the sleeves of your sweater. /
Glissando mit der Hand über die Tasten. Die Hand kann dabei mit einem Tuch oder dem Ärmel deines Pullovers geschützt werden.